For my Mum
Katie Taylor
For the gift of humour

Hackman!

love in buckets

Bill Houston

HarperCollins*Entertainment*

An Imprint of HarperCollins*Publishers*

HarperCollins*Entertainment*
An Imprint of HarperCollins*Publishers*
77–85 Fulham Palace Road,
Hammersmith, London W6 8JB
www.harpercollins.co.uk

Published by HarperCollins*Entertainment* 2006
1

Editor: Chris Smith

A catalogue record for this book
is available from the British Library

ISBN-13 978-0-00-720738-1
ISBN-10 0-00-720738-7

Set in Comic Sans

Printed and bound in Great Britain by
Butler and Tanner, Frome

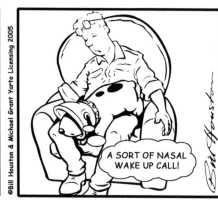

FULL METAL BUCKET

| Weather Report : |
| Raining Dogs and Dogs |
| Temp. 21° |
| Poo Count : Medium |

The Daily Bucket

Dogsbody
& Gruff
Accountants

Serving the City - www.hackmanthedog.com

EARLY RETIREMENT FOR ONE OF NEW YORK'S FINEST!

OFFICER KLUTZ DECIDES TO HANG UP HIS HANDCUFFS TWO YEARS EARLY.

OFFICER JERRY KLUTZ AND COMMANDER BORLAND EARLIER TODAY.

New York's finest said goodbye to one of their own today when Officer Jerry Klutz of the 51st Precinct decided to retire from the Force with two years left of his career. "It's a bit unusual to take such a drastic step," said Officer Klutz, "but recently I have been having headaches and flashbacks after a taking a "turn" in Central Park last month. I wake up at night and, I know this sounds crazy, but I seem to recall a large metal object and lots of banging!" Klutz went on, "I also got back to the Precinct that night with my hat turned around the wrong way; the guys loved it but I just have no idea what happened!" Jerry's immediate boss, Commander Thomas Borland, said, "It's always sad when an officer in the Force decides to call it a day, but this is particularly sad as Jerry Klutz has been attending a course with one of our psychologists to attempt to understand the problems he has experienced. We wish him well for the future and hope the banging in his head subsides soon." The psychologist wasn't available for comment.

BADBAD CASE COMES TO A CONCLUSION WHEN THE JUDGE PAYS THE FINE!

Kirk Badbad, the self acclaimed Hypno-shrink, was elated in court when the Judge fined him five thousand dollars and then announced to the jury he would pay the fine for Dr. Badbad. "I like to think that justice has prevailed here," said Badbad. "I've always maintained that I practise my work for free and my patients can pay if they wish; most are kind enough to offer a fee." The case came to court when Badbad was accused of forcing money from an 80-year-old Manhattan man with a sick budgie. Judge Gillies said, "I've come to the conclusion that Dr. Kirk Badbad is a menace to society and he's not the type of person we need practising in New York." When asked why he paid the fine for Dr. Badbad and let him walk free from the court, he said, "I have no idea why I let Dr.Badbad walk free; it was my intention to jail him but after a chat with him I felt it reasonable to pay his fine myself and let him go. I think I paid his parking ticket as well."

DR. KIRK BADBAD AND JUDGE GILLIES OUTSIDE THE COURT TODAY.

CITY VETS CONCERNED OVER NEW CANINE FASHION TREND!

New York veterinary surgeons issued a press release this morning stating their concerns at the new "must have" item flooding the canine fashion industry. "The plastic collar, or 'bucket' as it is affectionately known, is a medical item and not a Gucci or a Valentino necessity. In fact the wearing of the 'bucket' can cause great anxiety in pets." Please be warned.

TOTEM POLE ALIENS?
PARK RANGERS AMAZED AFTER FLASH FLOOD UNCOVERS FIND!

PARK RANGERS WITH THE UNUSUAL TOTEM POLE SCULPTURE.

Park Rangers Donny Hapwell and Bud Lewinsky were stopped in their tracks by a flash flood that had pushed a log across their path. On further investigation they noticed this was no ordinary log. Ranger Hapwell takes up the story: "We were amazed at the carvings on the log and we think it may be a totem pole and could be of Cherokee origin. The top looks like a dog of some sort but further down there seems to be a carving of a spaceship; we're very excited by this!" Ranger Lewinsky said: "My theory is that some sort of alien visited the Cherokees and they carved the totem pole in homage to him." At this point Ranger Lewinsky was removed from his office and accused of being under the influence of alcohol in the workplace. Ranger Hapwell refused to comment further.

MAMMOTH HAVING A REST SAY EXPERTS

After two years of study and a cost of thousands of dollars to the taxpayers of New York, archaeologists now believe that the famous exhibit at the Met, the "Sitting Mammoth", was "Only having a rest!" "This just isn't good enough," said our Natural History editor. "They've taken two years to come to this conclusion. Next they'll be saying that the dog was wearing a prehistoric bucket!"

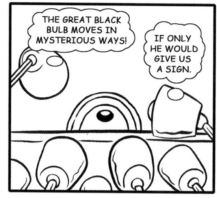

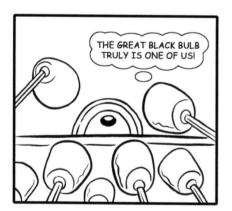

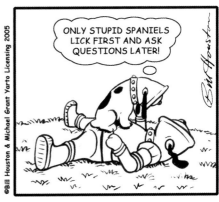

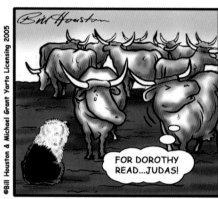

Weather Report :
Raining Dogs and Dogs
Temp. 21°
Poo Count : Medium

The Daily Bucket

Dogsbody
& Gruff
Accountants

Serving the City - www.hackmanthedog.com

LITTLE STONEHENGE DISCOVERED, EXPERTS AMAZED AT SIZE!

"EITHER THE PEOPLE WERE VERY SMALL OR SOMEONE MESSED UP BIG STYLE!" PROF. H. HOLLINGER

PROFESSOR HOLLINGER AND THE MINI STONEHENGE

"We're just amazed at how small it is!" said Professor Harry Hollinger of the Archaeological Society of Seattle. "We've got a fantastic find here and it's obviously a smaller version of the famous Stonehenge in Britain." He went on: "There are many theories as to the reason why its so small, but we tend to think it was probably an error on the part of it's creator. The "Neandrathal Man" who created this was probably not very confident in the sculpting department."
Cave paintings were discovered nearby which give the impression that the Moon was looked upon as a god to our artistic anncestors. Prof. Hollinger goes on: "We believe that these primitive paintings show the Moon in various states of fullness; there could be early signs of language too. In a crazy way it looks like the name Brian, but obviously that's just our modern view of a Stone Age marking. I don't believe for a moment the Moon was called Brian!"

SLUMP IN SALES LEAVES ANGLE POISE LAMPS IN THE DOLDRUMS.

Leslie Goldstein,68, the Sales Manager for forty years at "Many Hands Light Emporium" in downtown New York, has seen a few changes in his career selling fashionable lights to the good people of New York. "I admit I'm getting on a bit but I just can't see why there's been such a slump in sales of anglepoise lamps. Just look at those boys!" Mr.Goldstein likes to attribute human characteristics to his "boys". "Every morning I face their shades to the sky to give them a proud look and every evening they're back looking at the deck; it's sad I tell ya!" He went on: "The only one interested in them is this cute dog that stops by and has a little look at them. I guess it's the bright colors or something!" I've worked for the "Daily Bucket" for 10 years as Special Interest Editor," said Ellie McGlumphie, "and those lamps have touched my heart, so come on everyone and let's get Leslie's boys out there!" Contact the newspaper for details. 10% of any sales will be donated to "Burn Baby Burn", the Pyromaniacs Anonymous charity.

LESLIE GOLDSTEIN AND HIS "BOYS" AT "MANY HANDS LIGHT EMPORIUM"

SHRINK ON "CRUSADE" FINED $500 AND GIVEN 30 HOURS COMMUNITY SERVICE!

An unnamed NY psychiatrist was reprimanded in court today for driving without due care and attention to other motorists. He was arrested after arguing with a traffic officer regarding the merits of wearing a bucket in his "crusade" against the lack of knowledge and understanding of how dogs suffer when wearing a surgical collar, or "bucket". He was fined $500 and given community service after attempting to place the bucket on the judge's head in court.

CENTRAL PARK MODEL AEROPLANE BAN ENRAGES CITY MODELLERS!

ENRAGED MODELLERS GATHER AT CENTRAL PARK TODAY

Modellers of New York united today in a demonstration to vent their feelings against a temporary ban on flying remote-controlled aircraft in the park. Rocky Quinn, 23, of the Bronx said, "It's just crazy. So we hit some dog; it shouldn't have been in the way! It was a spaniel and they're not too clever; if it had been a West Highland Terrier we wouldn't even be having this discussion!" A spokesman for the Park Authority said in response, "This attitude is very short-sighted, as was the modeller in the incident, but Mr Quinn has to realise that the park is for everyone not just a few modellers. The dog was unharmed apart from some scratches to his nose. Fortunately he was wearing a "bucket" which took most of the impact. I do agree with Mr. Quinn about the West Highland Terrier though!"

ETHEL, THE BAG LADY WITH A HEART OF GOLD!

Ethel Herman, of no fixed abode, was awarded a "Heart of Gold" by NY Community Services today for her "diligence" and "effort" in giving our police dogs water, or "dinky woos" as Ethel puts it. "I've been giving dinky woos to our police dogs ever since I can remember. The officers are pleased because their doggies can get too hot in the back of the car." Ethel continued: "I've only ever known one likkle doggy refuse a dinky woo and that was recently. I think he was in disguise and didn't want his cover blown!" The "Heart of Gold" is actually made of tin but Ethel will treasure it just the same. "I was always getting mistaken for Ethel Merman in the old days, because of our names sounding the same. Some people say I look like her." Ethel continued to mutter about the old days as she left to fill up another doggy dinky woo. Thanks Ethel!

©Bill Houston & Michael Grant Yarto Licensing 2005

©Bill Houston & Michael Grant Yarto Licensing 2005

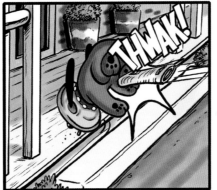

Introducing Hackman, the world's most adorable dog in
a bucket, in this debut collection of strips and cartoons.
Available wherever books are sold.

ISBN 0-00-720737-9

PLEASE LET THIS BE A DREAM!

EVEN BUCKETS
HAVE OFF DAYS!

BLACKFOOT
COUNTY 1852.

I KNOW HE'S DEFINITELY
THERE'S FOOD IN THIS!